S0-AXV-268

UP CLOSE CRITTERS

LEVEL READER

READING LEVEL
2
GRADES 1 TO 3

Photography © Igor Siwanowicz
Text © Dalmatian Press, LLC

Written by Kathryn Knight

Published by Dalmatian Press, LLC. All rights reserved.
Printed in Guangzhou, Guangdong, China.
Franklin, Tennessee 37068-2068. 1-866-418-2572.
No part of this book may be reproduced or copied in any form without written permission
from the copyright owner. CE14554/1211

There are critters
about us,
quite near us.
(They scout us.)

2

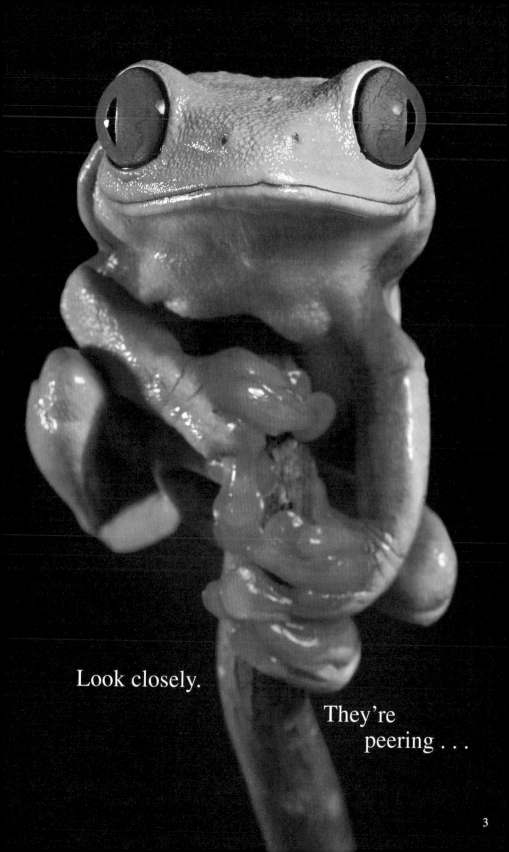

Look closely.

They're
peering . . .

. . . and leering . . .

4

. . . and sneering.

5

Sometimes they appear . . .

. . . and it's quite a surprise!

They stare with
odd eyes.

They glare with weird eyes . . .

9

. . . sometimes with eight eyes . . .

. . . or eyeballs of great size!

Some have coiled tails that are strange . . .

. . . and delightful.

13

Some have curved tails that are stingers.

(That's frightful!)

15

They may want to pop up . . .

. . . and show you their claws.

17

Pause awhile . . .

. . . and admire their paws.

It's such a treat to reach out . . .

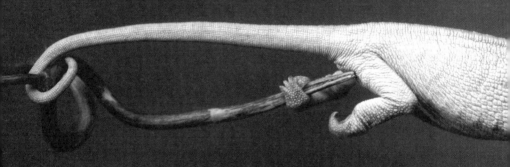

. . . and greet them!

They're really not *too* gross.

Get up close and meet them!

. . . well, maybe
not *too* close.

What are they?
cover: Cranwell's horned frog eye
  Ceratophrys cranwelli
pg 2, 5: crested gecko
  Rhacodactylus ciliatus
pg 3: red-eyed tree frog
  Agalychnis callidryas
pg 4: Fischer's chameleon
  Kinyongia fischeri
pgs 6–7: axolotl
  Ambystoma mexicanum
pg 8: giant African snail
  Achatina fulica
pg 9: pale giant horse fly
  Tabanus bovinus
pg 10: green jumping spider
  Mopsus mormon

pg 11: young crocodilian eye
pg 12: rough chameleon
  Chamaeleo rudis
pg 13: veiled chameleon tail
  Chamaeleo calyptratus
pgs 14–15: imperial scorpion tail
  Pandinus imperator
pgs 16–17: vampire crab
  Geosesarma sp.
pgs 18–19: fan-fingered gecko fingers
  Ptyodactylus guttatus
pgs 20–21: West Usambara two-horned chameleon
  Kinyongia multituberculata
pgs 22–23, 24: Cranwell's horned frog
  Ceratophrys cranwelli

24